Time

Words by Nina Filipek
Illustrated by Jan Smith

book-studio

Daisy wakes up early
in the morning.

"Time to get up,"
she says.

What is the time on
Daisy's alarm clock?

Daisy gets dressed and goes downstairs.

"Time for breakfast," says Mom.

What is the time on the kitchen clock?

Daisy and Mom go shopping.

They buy lots of things.

What is the time on the town clock?

"Time for a treat," says Mom.

She takes Daisy to Bert's cafe for lunch.

What is the time on the cafe clock?

After lunch, Daisy and Mom go to the playground.

Daisy plays on the swings.

What is the time on the playground clock?

Now it is time
to meet Dan.

The school bus
is on time.

What is the
time on
Mom's watch?

Daisy, Dan, and Mom go to see Grandma.

Grandma has baked a big cake. It's delicious.

What is the time on Grandma's clock?

Soon it is time to go home.

"Time for your bath, Daisy," says Mom.

Daisy has fun in the bathtub.

What is the time on the clock?

Daisy is very tired.

She falls fast asleep.

What is the time on Daisy's alarm clock?

The end